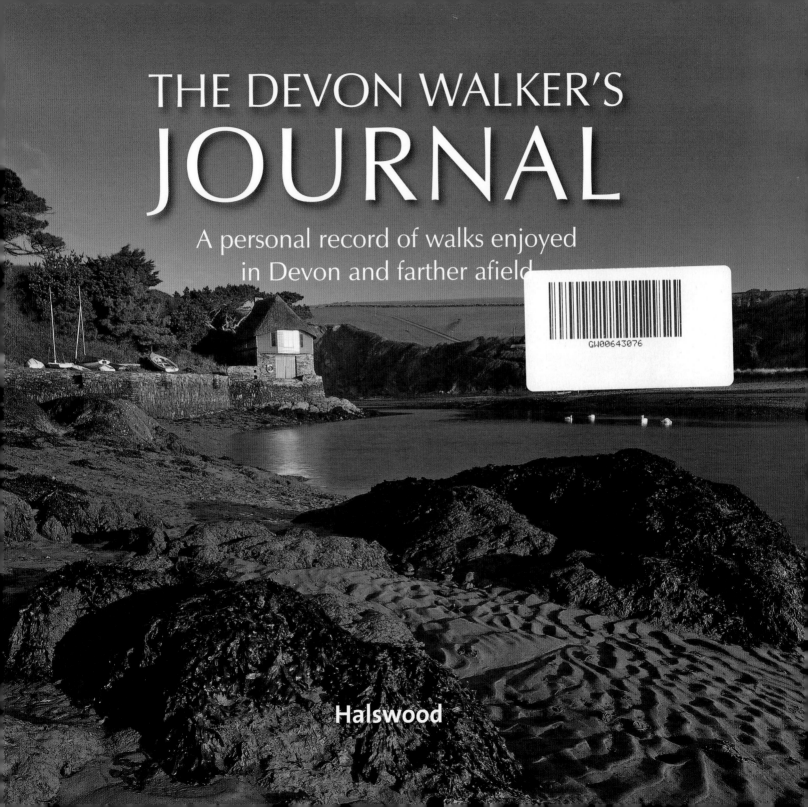

THE DEVON WALKER'S
JOURNAL

A personal record of walks enjoyed in Devon and farther afield

Halswood

Published by Halswood Stationers

British Library Cataloguing-in-Publication Data
A CIP record for this title is available from the
British Library

ISBN 978 0 85717 000 2

HALSWOOD STATIONERS
Halsgrove House,
Ryelands Industrial Estate,
Bagley Road, Wellington, Somerset TA21 9PZ
Tel: 01823 653777   Fax: 01823 216796
email: sales@halsgrove.com

Part of the Halsgrove group of companies
Information on all Halsgrove titles is available at:
www.halsgrove.com

Printed and bound in China by
Toppan Leefung Printing Ltd (0)

Front cover: *Sunrise from Honeybag Tor, Dartmoor.*
From *Dartmoor: A Winter's Tale*, Adrian Oakes.

Back cover: *The seafront at Teignmouth, dusk.*
From *The Romantic South Devon Coast*, Lee Pengelly.

Title page: *Thatched boathouse, Bantham.*
From *The Romantic South Devon Coast*, Lee Pengelly.

Right: *On the Two Moors Way, Exmoor.*
Anna Whittington.

THE DEVON WALKER'S JOURNAL

Walking is Britain's most popular outdoor recreation and more than half the population of Britain is recorded as walking for pleasure at least once a month. While some of us walk just to exercise the dog, many are more serious walkers, recognising not only the physical benefits of a bracing mile or two but also the 'rise in spirits' which come from getting outdoors and away from the concerns of daily life. Families, groups of friends and organised parties of ramblers, increasingly are finding the pleasures of planning and taking walks, at whatever distance, an inexpensive and highly rewarding activity.

In taking an exhilarating walk we need not rely on the car or public transport, for in England we are fortunate to live in a country in which public footpaths and rights of way have for centuries provided freedom of access. More recent legislation has increased this 'right to roam', opening up areas beyond the confines of designated routes. Local authorities, in part impelled by interested rambling organisations, but also through recognising the overall social benefits of walking, have invested in keeping footpaths in good order, in waymarking and providing useful local walks leaflets. The market in walking books appears to know no bounds.

This *Walker's Journal* provides an opportunity for the dedicated walker to keep a record of where and when they walked, and with whom. That it carries a title relating to a particular county is no reason why the walker should not venture farther afield, simply that the journal represents their 'home patch' or a region close to their heart. The photographs, as well as adding to the attractive design of the journal are included as an inspiration to explore the superb countryside on our doorstep.

Our aim has been to make the use of the *Walker's Journal* as flexible as possible, allowing the user to decide how best to create a record of their walking journeys. For some, a single journal may last a year or more, perhaps for others this journal may be one that builds into a number of volumes. As with a diary, it will act as an *aide-memoire*, but more than that we hope it will give hours of pleasure when, on re-reading in future years, it will help recall past walks long forgotten, and warm memories of good friends and companionship.

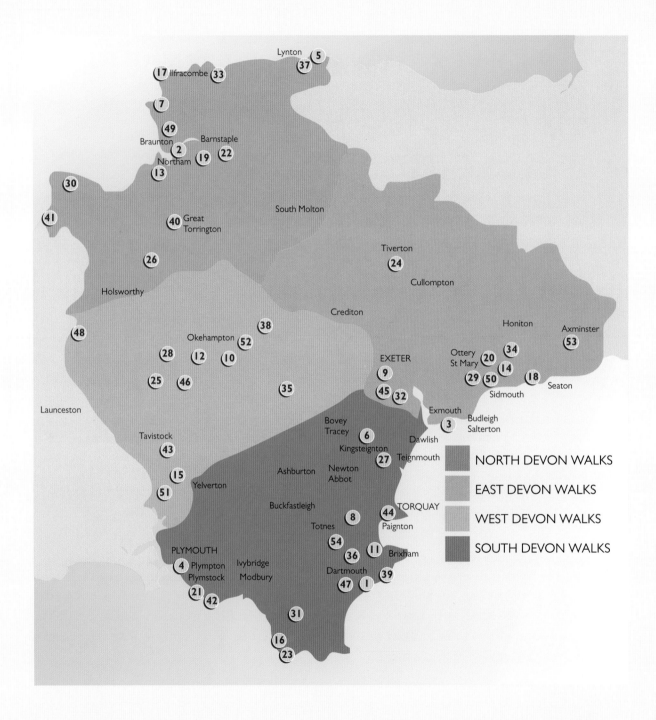

Lynton (5) (37)

(17) Ilfracombe (33)

(7)

(49)

Braunton (2) (19) (22) Barnstaple

Northam

(13)

(30)

(41)

South Molton

(40) Great Torrington

(26)

Tiverton

(24)

Cullompton

Holsworthy

Crediton

Honiton

Axminster

(48)

(38)

Okehampton (52)

(53)

(28) (12) (10)

EXETER

Ottery St Mary (20) (34)

(9)

(29) (50) (14)

(25) (46)

(35)

(45) (32)

(18)

Seaton

Sidmouth

Launceston

Exmouth

(3)

Budleigh Salterton

Bovey Tracey

Dawlish

Tavistock

(6)

Kingsteignton

(43)

(27) Teignmouth

Ashburton Newton Abbot

(15)

Yelverton

(51)

Buckfastleigh

TORQUAY

(8) (44)

Paignton

Totnes

(54)

PLYMOUTH

(11) Brixham

(36)

(4) Plympton Plymstock

Ivybridge Modbury

Dartmouth

(39)

(21)

(47) (1)

(42)

(31)

(16)

(23)

NORTH DEVON WALKS

EAST DEVON WALKS

WEST DEVON WALKS

SOUTH DEVON WALKS

SOME INTERESTING WALKS IN DEVON

The map opposite and walks listed below are based upon Devon County Council's suggested walks, complete details of which, including directions and maps, can be found on the websites www.visitdevon.co.uk and www.devon.gov.uk, both of which sites contain invaluable information for walkers. They are included here in order to help those who might not otherwise have a wide knowledge of where to walk in Devon.

1	Dartmouth and the Dart Valley	28	Two Castles Trail
2	Torridge Estuary Rail Trail	29	Newton Poppleford and Hawkerland
3	The Sid Valley	30	Clovelly's Western Woods and Cliffs
4	Plymouth's Forts and Castles	31	Salcombe and Snapes Point
5	Around Lynmouth	32	Exeter to Starcross
6	Templer Way Heritage Trail	33	Ilfracombe and the Torrs
7	Baggy Point	34	Sidbury and Fire Beacon Hill
8	Middle Dart Valley	35	The Teign Gorge (Two Moors Way)
9	Exeter and the Exe Valley Way	36	Dart Valley and Greenway House
10	The Ernest Bassett Walk, Okehampton	37	Lynton and the Valley of the Rocks
11	Torbay and the Dart Valley	38	Southern Railway Dartmoor Walk
12	Meldon Viaduct, Okehampton	39	Brixham and Berry Head
13	Westward Ho! and the South West Coast Path	40	Around Torrington
14	The River Otter Valley	41	Hartland Point and the South West Coast Path
15	Tamar Valley Discovery Trail	42	Around Noss Mayo
16	Hope Cove	43	The West Devon Way
17	Mortehoe and the North Devon Coast	44	Hidden Torquay
18	Beer Head and Seaton	45	The Exeter Green Circle
19	Tarka Trail and the Taw Valley	46	Lydford and The West Devon Way
20	The River Sid Valley	47	Blackpool and the South West Coast Path
21	Wembury to Plymouth Walk	48	Tetcott – Jester Walk
22	Barnstaple to Landkey (Tarka Trail)	49	Saunton Down
23	The Salcombe Estuary	50	Sidmouth and the Jurassic Coast
24	The Middle Exe Valley	51	The Bere Peninsula
25	Lydford to Mary Tavy	52	Two Museums Walk - Sticklepath/Okehampton
26	The Ruby Trail	53	Colyton and The East Devon Way
27	The Templer Way	54	Totnes to Sharpham

INDEX OF WALKS

Checking the map along the Two Moors Way.
Anna Whittington

INDEX OF WALKS

REMARKS AND INCIDENTS:

Walked to Cadover
Bridge, probably a
four mile walk
through forests
& along a river
We walked though
Oak Woods
which was wonderful.
The river was
We lost each other
& found each other
back at the car.
the river we walked
along is called the River Plym

WALK 1

From: 2/1/2017

To:

Date:

Weather:

Distance:

Duration: hrs mins

Companions:

OAK leaf

Newton Ferrers, South Devon, with Dartmoor on the horizon.
Jason Hawkes

9

WALK

From:

To:

Date:

Weather:

Distance:

Duration: hrs   mins

Companions:

REMARKS AND INCIDENTS:

REMARKS AND INCIDENTS:

_____
_____
_____
_____
_____
_____
_____
_____
_____
_____
_____
_____
_____

WALK

From:

To:

Date:

Weather:

Distance:

Duration: hrs   mins

Companions:

_____
_____
_____
_____
_____
_____
_____
_____
_____
_____
_____

WALK

From:

To:

Date:

Weather:

Distance:

Duration: hrs   mins

Companions:

REMARKS AND INCIDENTS:

_____
_____
_____
_____
_____
_____
_____
_____
_____
_____
_____
_____
_____
_____

WALK

From:

To:

Date:

Weather:

Distance:

Duration: hrs   mins

Companions:

_____
_____
_____
_____
_____
_____
_____
_____
_____
_____
_____
_____

WALK

From:

To:

Date:

Weather:

Distance:

Duration: hrs   mins

Companions:

REMARKS AND INCIDENTS:

_____
_____
_____
_____
_____
_____
_____
_____
_____
_____
_____
_____
_____

WALK

From:

To:

Date:

Weather:

Distance:

Duration: hrs   mins

Companions:

_____
_____
_____
_____
_____
_____
_____
_____
_____
_____
_____

REMARKS AND INCIDENTS:

_____
_____
_____
_____
_____
_____
_____
_____
_____
_____
_____
_____
_____
_____

WALK

From:

To:

Date:

Weather:

Distance:

Duration: hrs   mins

Companions:

_____
_____
_____
_____
_____
_____
_____
_____
_____
_____
_____
_____

Superb walking country on the South West Coast Path
at the Valley of Rocks, North Devon.
Jason Hawkes

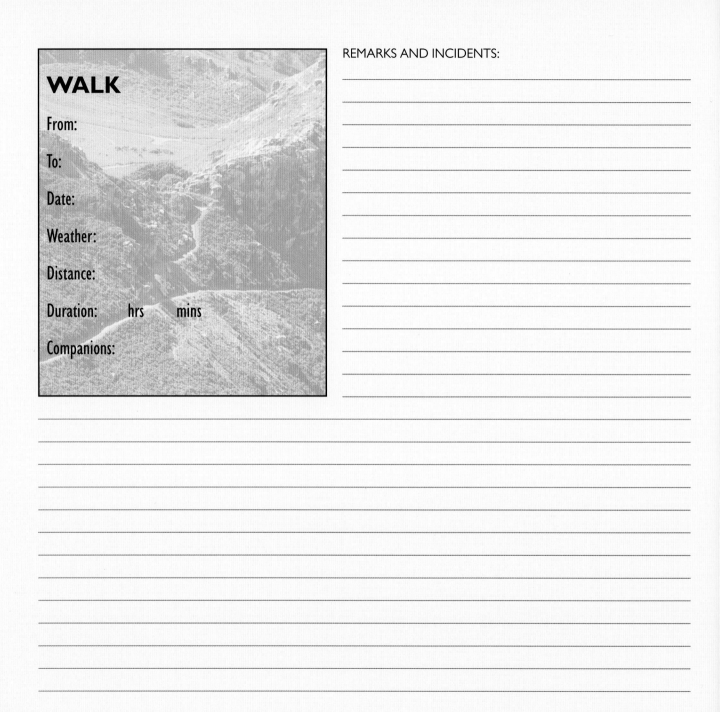

WALK

From:

To:

Date:

Weather:

Distance:

Duration: hrs mins

Companions:

REMARKS AND INCIDENTS:

REMARKS AND INCIDENTS:

WALK

From:

To:

Date:

Weather:

Distance:

Duration: hrs   mins

Companions:

WALK

From:

To:

Date:

Weather:

Distance:

Duration: hrs   mins

Companions:

REMARKS AND INCIDENTS:

REMARKS AND INCIDENTS:

_____

_____

_____

_____

_____

_____

_____

_____

_____

_____

_____

_____

WALK

From:

To:

Date:

Weather:

Distance:

Duration: hrs   mins

Companions:

_____

_____

_____

_____

_____

_____

_____

_____

_____

_____

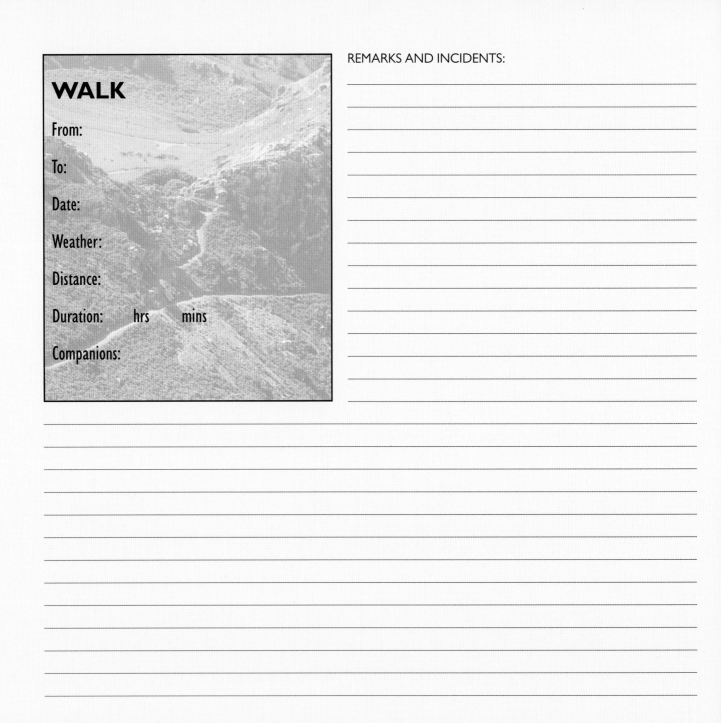

WALK

From:

To:

Date:

Weather:

Distance:

Duration: hrs   mins

Companions:

REMARKS AND INCIDENTS:

REMARKS AND INCIDENTS:

WALK

From:

To:

Date:

Weather:

Distance:

Duration: hrs   mins

Companions:

REMARKS AND INCIDENTS:

_____
_____
_____
_____
_____
_____
_____
_____
_____
_____
_____
_____
_____

WALK

From:

To:

Date:

Weather:

Distance:

Duration: hrs   mins

Companions:

_____
_____
_____
_____
_____
_____
_____
_____
_____
_____
_____
_____
_____
_____
_____
_____

Sunrise from Honeybag Tor, Dartmoor.
Adrian Oakes

WALK

From:

To:

Date:

Weather:

Distance:

Duration: hrs   mins

Companions:

REMARKS AND INCIDENTS:

REMARKS AND INCIDENTS:

WALK

From:

To:

Date:

Weather:

Distance:

Duration: hrs   mins

Companions:

WALK

From:

To:

Date:

Weather:

Distance:

Duration: hrs   mins

Companions:

REMARKS AND INCIDENTS:

REMARKS AND INCIDENTS:

_____
_____
_____
_____
_____
_____
_____
_____
_____
_____
_____
_____
_____

WALK

From:

To:

Date:

Weather:

Distance:

Duration: hrs   mins

Companions:

_____
_____
_____
_____
_____
_____
_____
_____
_____
_____
_____
_____

WALK

From:

To:

Date:

Weather:

Distance:

Duration: hrs   mins

Companions:

REMARKS AND INCIDENTS:

REMARKS AND INCIDENTS:

_____
_____
_____
_____
_____
_____
_____
_____
_____
_____
_____
_____
_____

WALK

From:

To:

Date:

Weather:

Distance:

Duration: hrs   mins

Companions:

_____
_____
_____
_____
_____
_____
_____
_____
_____
_____
_____
_____

REMARKS AND INCIDENTS:

WALK

From:

To:

Date:

Weather:

Distance:

Duration: hrs   mins

Companions:

The seafront at Teignmouth, dusk.
Lee Pengelly

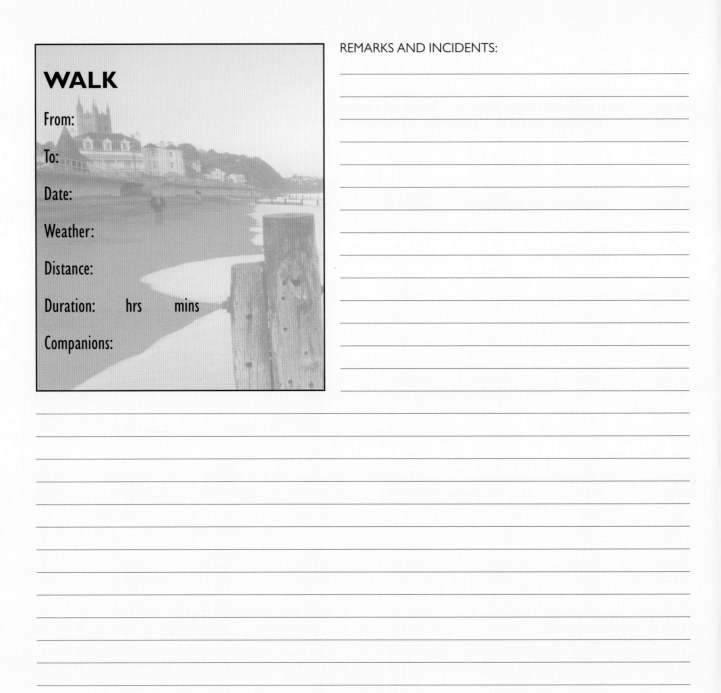

WALK

From:

To:

Date:

Weather:

Distance:

Duration: hrs   mins

Companions:

REMARKS AND INCIDENTS:

REMARKS AND INCIDENTS:

WALK

From:

To:

Date:

Weather:

Distance:

Duration: hrs   mins

Companions:

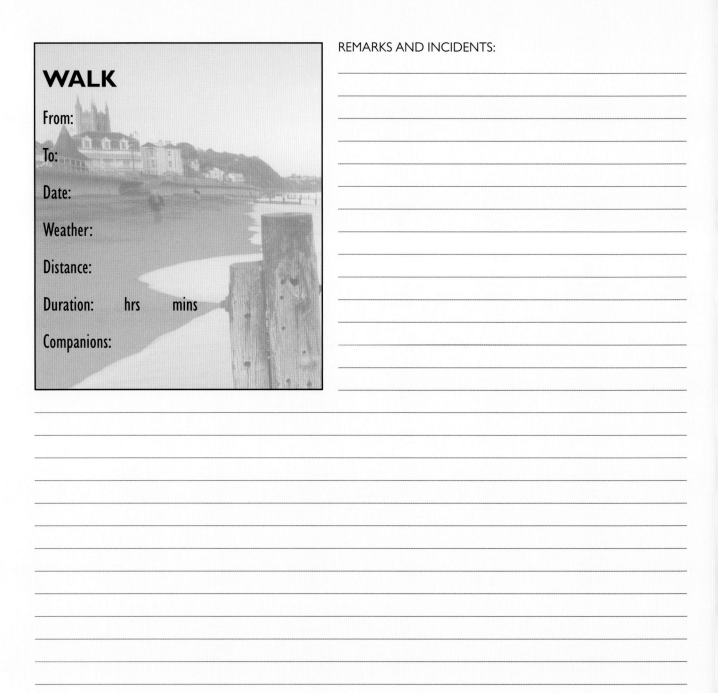

WALK

From:

To:

Date:

Weather:

Distance:

Duration:　　hrs　　mins

Companions:

REMARKS AND INCIDENTS:

REMARKS AND INCIDENTS:

WALK

From:

To:

Date:

Weather:

Distance:

Duration: hrs mins

Companions:

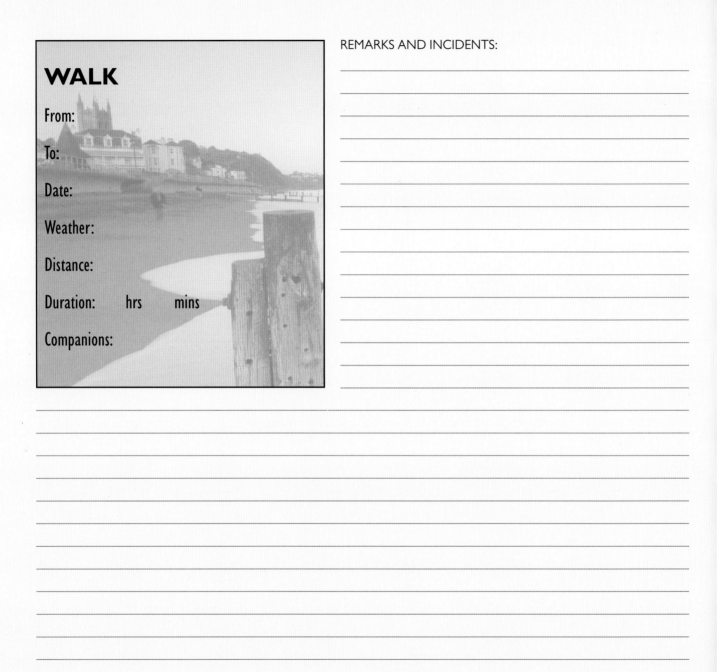

WALK

From:

To:

Date:

Weather:

Distance:

Duration: hrs   mins

Companions:

REMARKS AND INCIDENTS:

REMARKS AND INCIDENTS:

_____
_____
_____
_____
_____
_____
_____
_____
_____
_____
_____
_____

WALK

From:

To:

Date:

Weather:

Distance:

Duration: hrs   mins

Companions:

_____
_____
_____
_____
_____
_____
_____
_____
_____
_____

REMARKS AND INCIDENTS:

_____
_____
_____
_____
_____
_____
_____
_____
_____
_____
_____
_____
_____

WALK

From:

To:

Date:

Weather:

Distance:

Duration: hrs   mins

Companions:

_____
_____
_____
_____
_____
_____
_____
_____
_____
_____
_____
_____

Waterfall on the East Okement River.
David Elliott

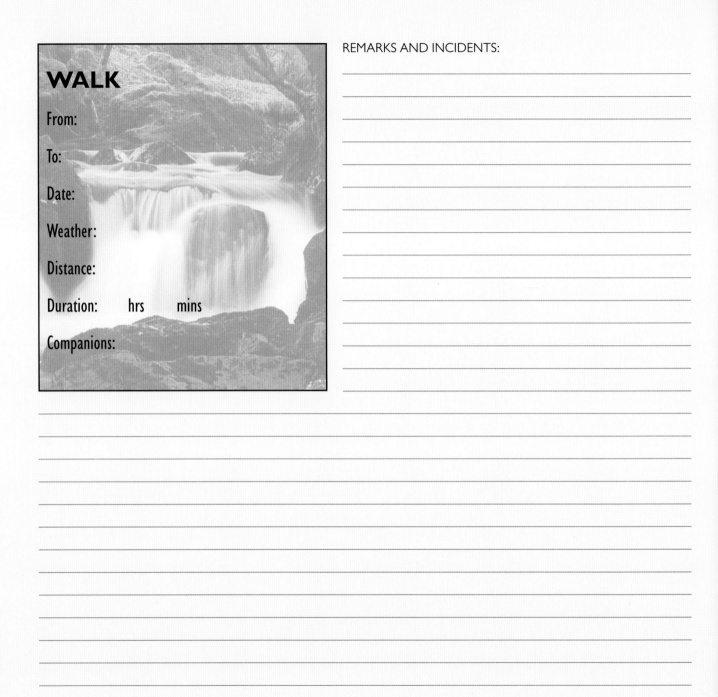

WALK

From:

To:

Date:

Weather:

Distance:

Duration: hrs   mins

Companions:

REMARKS AND INCIDENTS:

REMARKS AND INCIDENTS:

WALK

From:

To:

Date:

Weather:

Distance:

Duration:　　　hrs　　　mins

Companions:

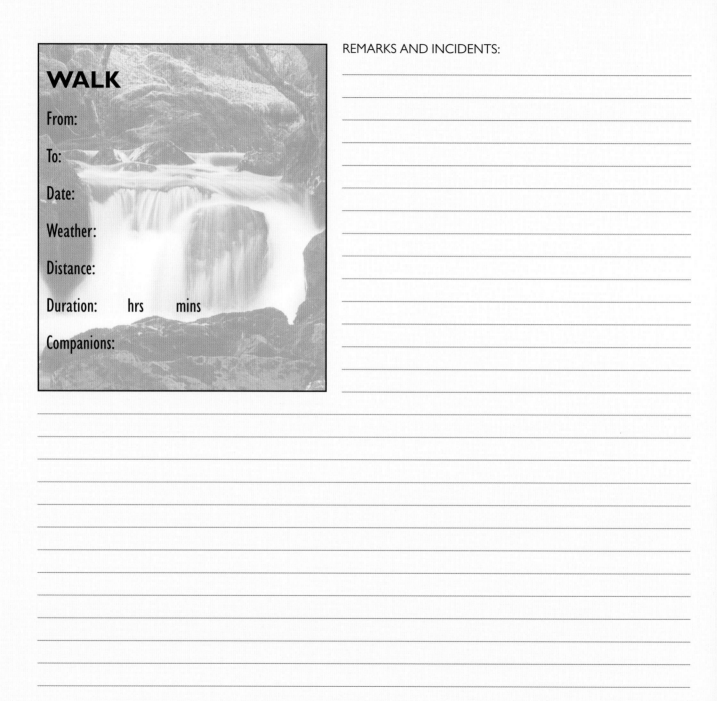

WALK

From:

To:

Date:

Weather:

Distance:

Duration: hrs   mins

Companions:

REMARKS AND INCIDENTS:

REMARKS AND INCIDENTS:

_____
_____
_____
_____
_____
_____
_____
_____
_____
_____

WALK

From:

To:

Date:

Weather:

Distance:

Duration: hrs   mins

Companions:

_____
_____
_____
_____
_____
_____
_____
_____
_____
_____
_____
_____

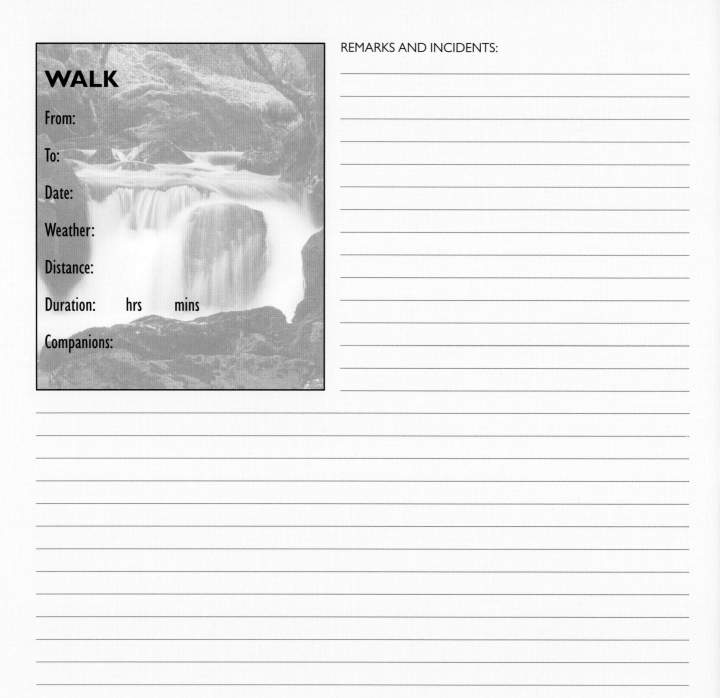

WALK

From:

To:

Date:

Weather:

Distance:

Duration: hrs   mins

Companions:

REMARKS AND INCIDENTS:

REMARKS AND INCIDENTS:

_____

_____

_____

_____

_____

_____

_____

_____

_____

_____

_____

_____

WALK

From:

To:

Date:

Weather:

Distance:

Duration: hrs   mins

Companions:

_____

_____

_____

_____

_____

_____

_____

_____

_____

_____

_____

REMARKS AND INCIDENTS:

_____
_____
_____
_____
_____
_____
_____
_____
_____
_____
_____
_____

WALK

From:

To:

Date:

Weather:

Distance:

Duration: hrs   mins

Companions:

_____
_____
_____
_____
_____
_____
_____
_____
_____
_____

Dartmoor Summer, near Foggintor.
Carol Ballenger

WALK

From:

To:

Date:

Weather:

Distance:

Duration: hrs   mins

Companions:

REMARKS AND INCIDENTS:

REMARKS AND INCIDENTS:

_____
_____
_____
_____
_____
_____
_____
_____
_____
_____
_____
_____
_____
_____

WALK

From:

To:

Date:

Weather:

Distance:

Duration: hrs   mins

Companions:

_____
_____
_____
_____
_____
_____
_____
_____
_____
_____
_____
_____

WALK

From:

To:

Date:

Weather:

Distance:

Duration: hrs   mins

Companions:

REMARKS AND INCIDENTS:

REMARKS AND INCIDENTS:

_____
_____
_____
_____
_____
_____
_____
_____
_____
_____
_____
_____

WALK

From:

To:

Date:

Weather:

Distance:

Duration: hrs   mins

Companions:

_____
_____
_____
_____
_____
_____
_____
_____
_____
_____
_____

WALK

From:

To:

Date:

Weather:

Distance:

Duration: hrs   mins

Companions:

REMARKS AND INCIDENTS:

REMARKS AND INCIDENTS:

_____
_____
_____
_____
_____
_____
_____
_____
_____
_____
_____
_____
_____

WALK

From:

To:

Date:

Weather:

Distance:

Duration: hrs   mins

Companions:

_____
_____
_____
_____
_____
_____
_____
_____
_____
_____
_____

REMARKS AND INCIDENTS:

_____
_____
_____
_____
_____
_____
_____
_____
_____
_____
_____
_____
_____
_____

WALK

From:

To:

Date:

Weather:

Distance:

Duration: hrs   mins

Companions:

_____
_____
_____
_____
_____
_____
_____
_____
_____
_____
_____
_____

The footpath from Woody Bay, North Devon.
David Elliott

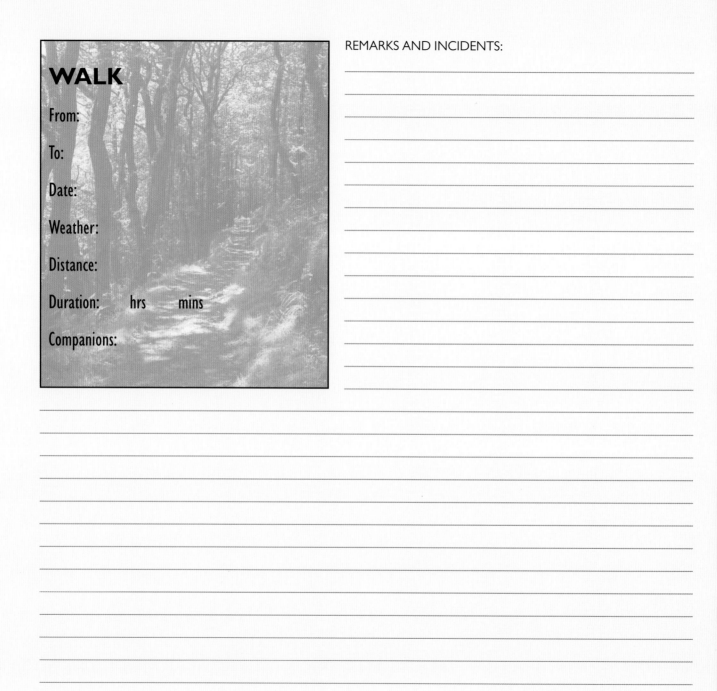

WALK

From:

To:

Date:

Weather:

Distance:

Duration: hrs mins

Companions:

REMARKS AND INCIDENTS:

REMARKS AND INCIDENTS:

_____
_____
_____
_____
_____
_____
_____
_____
_____
_____
_____
_____
_____
_____

WALK

From:

To:

Date:

Weather:

Distance:

Duration: hrs   mins

Companions:

_____
_____
_____
_____
_____
_____
_____
_____
_____
_____
_____
_____
_____

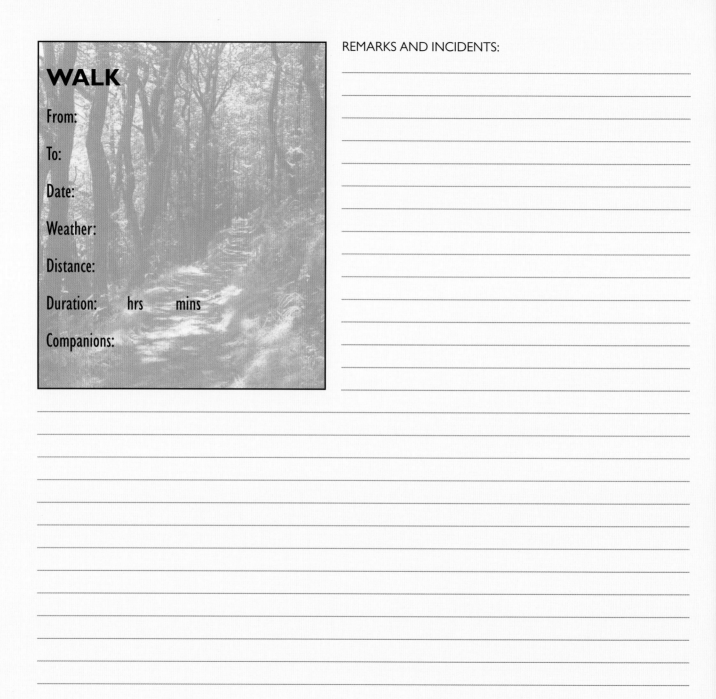

WALK

From:

To:

Date:

Weather:

Distance:

Duration:　　hrs　　mins

Companions:

REMARKS AND INCIDENTS:

REMARKS AND INCIDENTS:

_____

_____

_____

_____

_____

_____

_____

_____

_____

_____

_____

_____

_____

WALK

From:

To:

Date:

Weather:

Distance:

Duration: hrs   mins

Companions:

_____

_____

_____

_____

_____

_____

_____

_____

_____

_____

_____

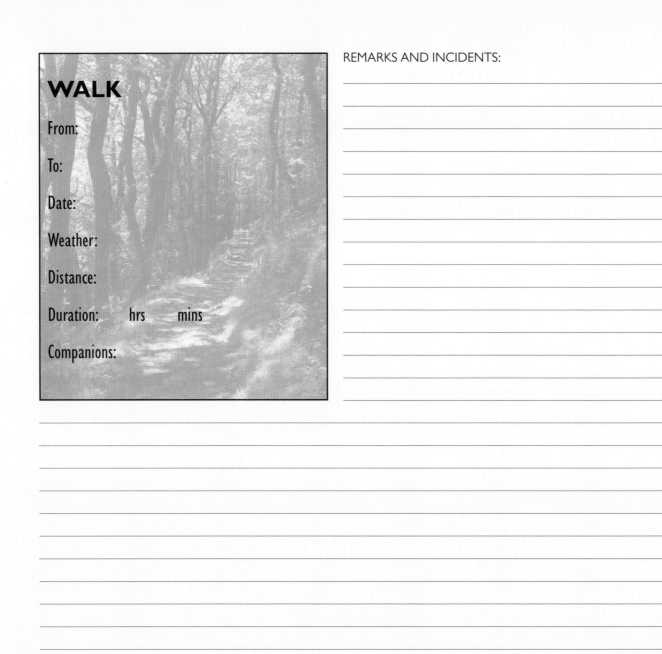

WALK

From:

To:

Date:

Weather:

Distance:

Duration: hrs   mins

Companions:

REMARKS AND INCIDENTS:

REMARKS AND INCIDENTS:

WALK

From:

To:

Date:

Weather:

Distance:

Duration: hrs   mins

Companions:

REMARKS AND INCIDENTS:

_____
_____
_____
_____
_____
_____
_____
_____
_____
_____
_____
_____
_____
_____

WALK

From:

To:

Date:

Weather:

Distance:

Duration: hrs   mins

Companions:

_____
_____
_____
_____
_____
_____
_____
_____
_____
_____
_____
_____

Faithful companions: a brief rest on a snowy day.
Jack Paynter

WALK

From:

To:

Date:

Weather:

Distance:

Duration: hrs   mins

Companions:

REMARKS AND INCIDENTS:

REMARKS AND INCIDENTS:

_____
_____
_____
_____
_____
_____
_____
_____
_____
_____
_____
_____
_____

WALK

From:

To:

Date:

Weather:

Distance:

Duration: hrs   mins

Companions:

_____
_____
_____
_____
_____
_____
_____
_____
_____
_____
_____
_____

WALK

From:

To:

Date:

Weather:

Distance:

Duration:　　hrs　　mins

Companions:

REMARKS AND INCIDENTS:

REMARKS AND INCIDENTS:

WALK

From:

To:

Date:

Weather:

Distance:

Duration: hrs   mins

Companions:

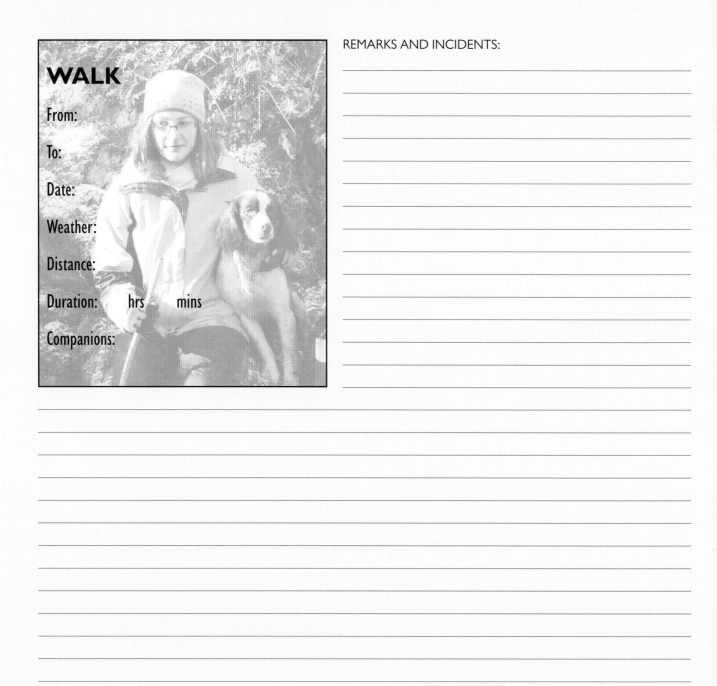

WALK

From:

To:

Date:

Weather:

Distance:

Duration: hrs   mins

Companions:

REMARKS AND INCIDENTS:

REMARKS AND INCIDENTS:

_____
_____
_____
_____
_____
_____
_____
_____
_____
_____
_____
_____
_____

WALK

From:

To:

Date:

Weather:

Distance:

Duration: hrs   mins

Companions:

_____
_____
_____
_____
_____
_____
_____
_____
_____
_____
_____
_____
_____

REMARKS AND INCIDENTS:

_____

_____

_____

_____

_____

_____

_____

_____

_____

_____

_____

_____

_____

WALK

From:

To:

Date:

Weather:

Distance:

Duration: hrs   mins

Companions:

_____

_____

_____

_____

_____

_____

_____

_____

_____

_____

_____

Start Point, South Devon, is the most southerly point in the British Isles and
is thus a key objective for walkers on the South West Coast Path.
Jason Hawkes

WALK

From:

To:

Date:

Weather:

Distance:

Duration: hrs   mins

Companions:

REMARKS AND INCIDENTS:

74

REMARKS AND INCIDENTS:

_____
_____
_____
_____
_____
_____
_____
_____
_____
_____
_____
_____

WALK

From:

To:

Date:

Weather:

Distance:

Duration: hrs   mins

Companions:

_____
_____
_____
_____
_____
_____
_____
_____
_____
_____
_____
_____

WALK

From:

To:

Date:

Weather:

Distance:

Duration: hrs   mins

Companions:

REMARKS AND INCIDENTS:

REMARKS AND INCIDENTS:

_____
_____
_____
_____
_____
_____
_____
_____
_____
_____
_____

WALK

From:

To:

Date:

Weather:

Distance:

Duration: hrs   mins

Companions:

_____
_____
_____
_____
_____
_____
_____
_____
_____
_____
_____
_____

WALK

From:

To:

Date:

Weather:

Distance:

Duration: hrs   mins

Companions:

REMARKS AND INCIDENTS:

REMARKS AND INCIDENTS:

_____
_____
_____
_____
_____
_____
_____
_____
_____
_____
_____
_____
_____
_____

WALK

From:

To:

Date:

Weather:

Distance:

Duration: hrs   mins

Companions:

_____
_____
_____
_____
_____
_____
_____
_____
_____
_____
_____

REMARKS AND INCIDENTS:

_____

_____

_____

_____

_____

_____

_____

_____

_____

_____

_____

WALK

From:

To:

Date:

Weather:

Distance:

Duration: hrs   mins

Companions:

_____

_____

_____

_____

_____

_____

_____

_____

_____

_____

Walkers on the South West Coast Path near Lynton, North Devon.
David Elliott.

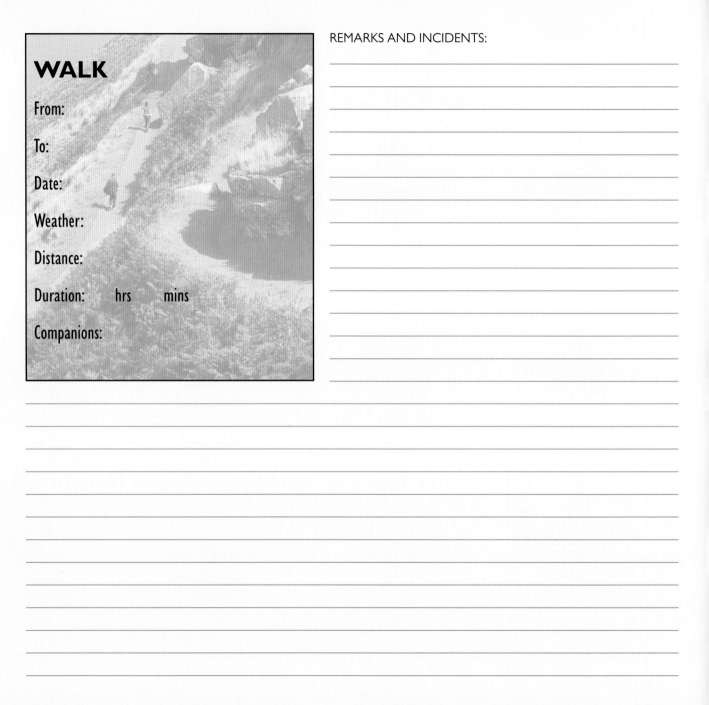

WALK

From:

To:

Date:

Weather:

Distance:

Duration: hrs   mins

Companions:

REMARKS AND INCIDENTS:

REMARKS AND INCIDENTS:

_____
_____
_____
_____
_____
_____
_____
_____
_____
_____
_____
_____
_____

WALK

From:

To:

Date:

Weather:

Distance:

Duration: hrs   mins

Companions:

_____
_____
_____
_____
_____
_____
_____
_____
_____
_____

WALK

From:

To:

Date:

Weather:

Distance:

Duration: hrs   mins

Companions:

REMARKS AND INCIDENTS:

_____
_____
_____
_____
_____
_____
_____
_____
_____
_____
_____
_____
_____
_____

WALK

From:

To:

Date:

Weather:

Distance:

Duration: hrs   mins

Companions:

_____
_____
_____
_____
_____
_____
_____
_____
_____
_____

WALK

From:

To:

Date:

Weather:

Distance:

Duration: hrs   mins

Companions:

REMARKS AND INCIDENTS:

REMARKS AND INCIDENTS:

_____
_____
_____
_____
_____
_____
_____
_____
_____
_____
_____
_____
_____

WALK

From:

To:

Date:

Weather:

Distance:

Duration: hrs   mins

Companions:

_____
_____
_____
_____
_____
_____
_____
_____
_____
_____
_____
_____

REMARKS AND INCIDENTS:

_____
_____
_____
_____
_____
_____
_____
_____
_____
_____
_____

WALK

From:

To:

Date:

Weather:

Distance:

Duration: hrs   mins

Companions:

_____
_____
_____
_____
_____
_____
_____
_____
_____
_____
_____

The majestic Hound Tor, Dartmoor, a favourite starting point
for walkers visiting this part of the moor.
Jack Paynter

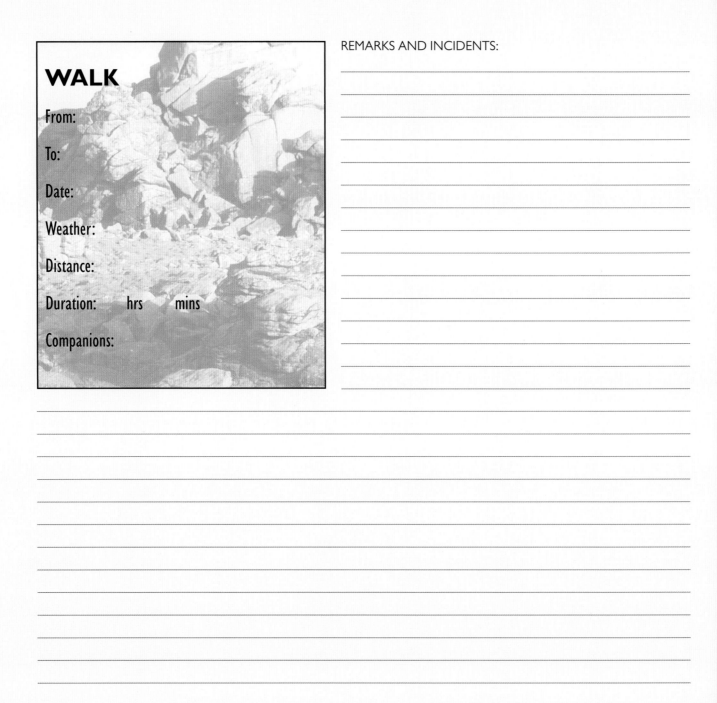

WALK

From:

To:

Date:

Weather:

Distance:

Duration: hrs   mins

Companions:

REMARKS AND INCIDENTS:

REMARKS AND INCIDENTS:

WALK

From:

To:

Date:

Weather:

Distance:

Duration: hrs   mins

Companions:

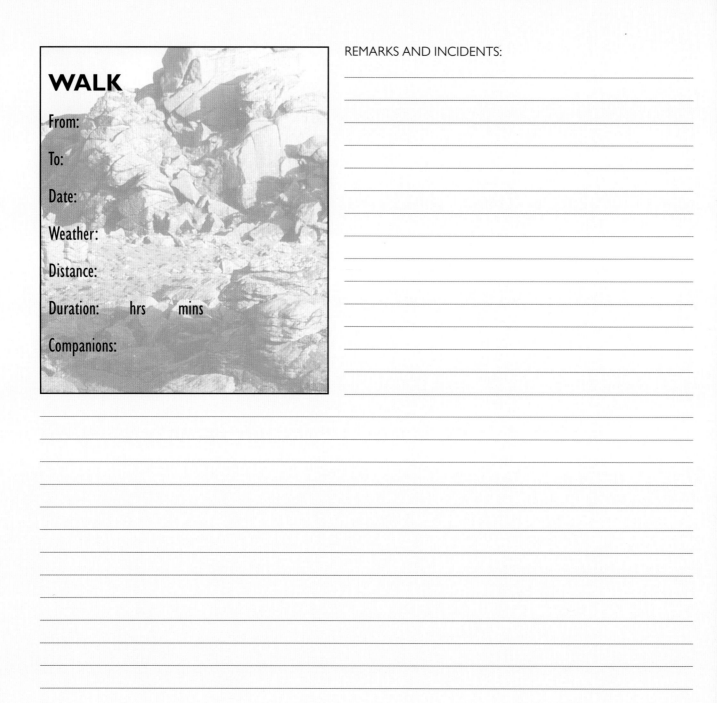

WALK

From:

To:

Date:

Weather:

Distance:

Duration: hrs   mins

Companions:

REMARKS AND INCIDENTS:

REMARKS AND INCIDENTS:

_____
_____
_____
_____
_____
_____
_____
_____
_____
_____
_____
_____
_____

WALK

From:

To:

Date:

Weather:

Distance:

Duration: hrs   mins

Companions:

_____
_____
_____
_____
_____
_____
_____
_____
_____
_____
_____
_____

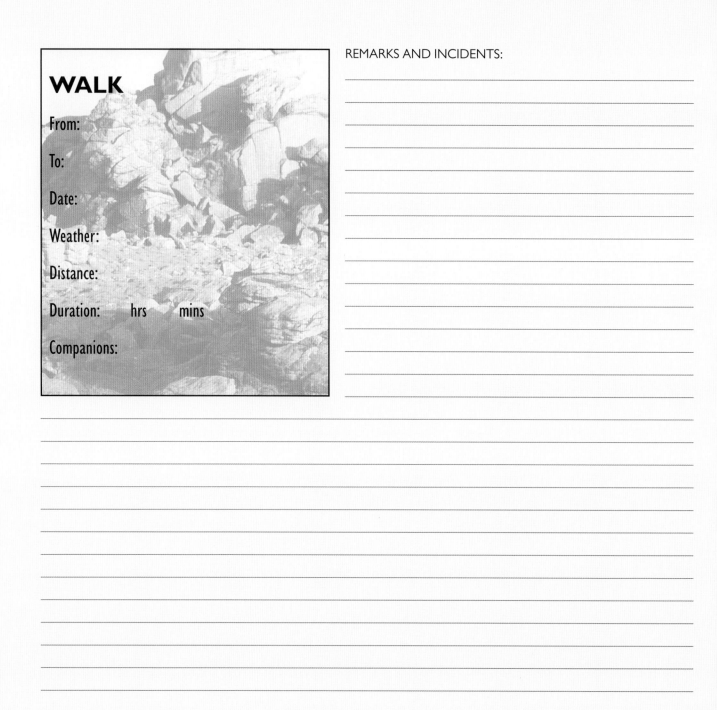

WALK

From:

To:

Date:

Weather:

Distance:

Duration: hrs   mins

Companions:

REMARKS AND INCIDENTS:

REMARKS AND INCIDENTS:

_____
_____
_____
_____
_____
_____
_____
_____
_____
_____
_____
_____
_____

WALK

From:

To:

Date:

Weather:

Distance:

Duration: hrs   mins

Companions:

_____
_____
_____
_____
_____
_____
_____
_____
_____
_____

REMARKS AND INCIDENTS:

_____
_____
_____
_____
_____
_____
_____
_____
_____
_____
_____

WALK

From:

To:

Date:

Weather:

Distance:

Duration: hrs   mins

Companions:

_____
_____
_____
_____
_____
_____
_____
_____
_____
_____
_____
_____

Drying boots at the end of the day.
Anna Whittington

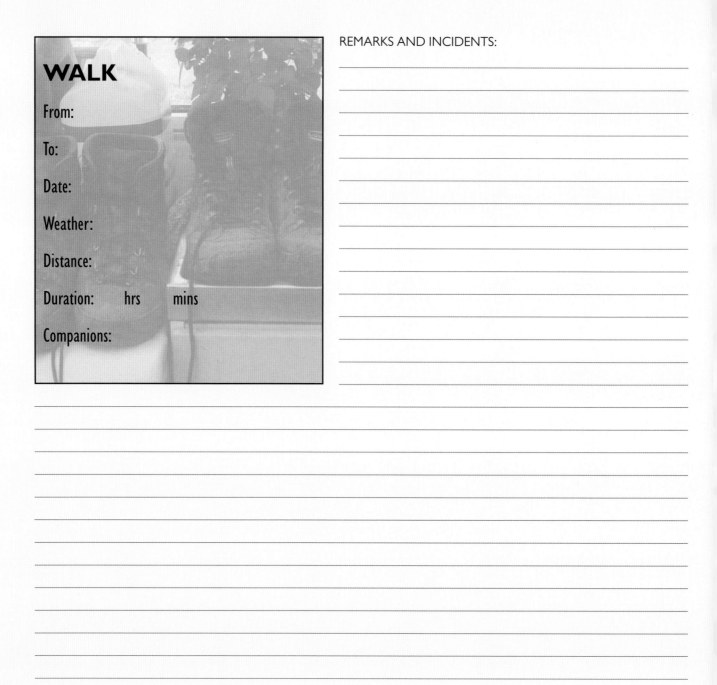

WALK

From:

To:

Date:

Weather:

Distance:

Duration: hrs mins

Companions:

REMARKS AND INCIDENTS:

REMARKS AND INCIDENTS:

_____
_____
_____
_____
_____
_____
_____
_____
_____
_____
_____
_____
_____
_____

WALK

From:

To:

Date:

Weather:

Distance:

Duration: hrs   mins

Companions:

_____
_____
_____
_____
_____
_____
_____
_____
_____
_____
_____
_____

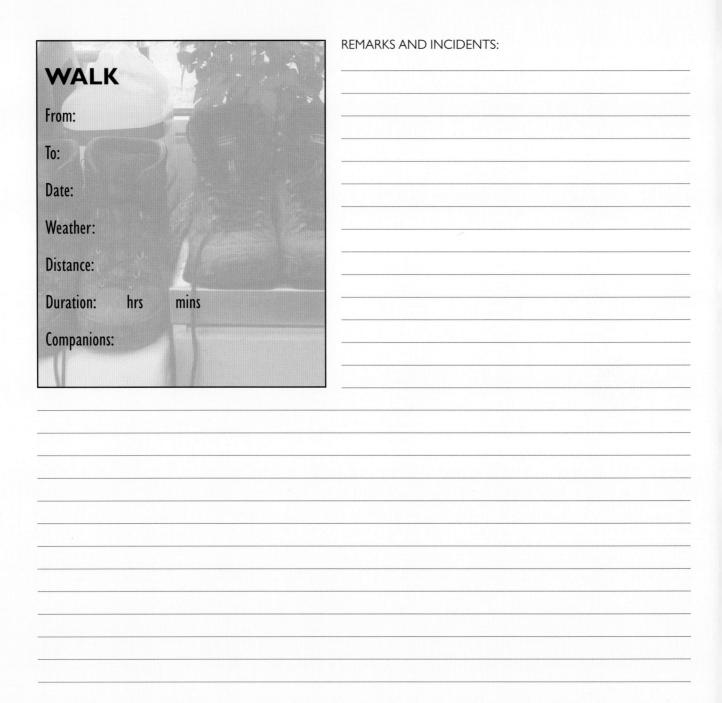

WALK

From:

To:

Date:

Weather:

Distance:

Duration:　　hrs　　mins

Companions:

REMARKS AND INCIDENTS:

REMARKS AND INCIDENTS:

_____
_____
_____
_____
_____
_____
_____
_____
_____
_____
_____
_____

WALK

From:

To:

Date:

Weather:

Distance:

Duration: hrs   mins

Companions:

_____
_____
_____
_____
_____
_____
_____
_____
_____
_____
_____

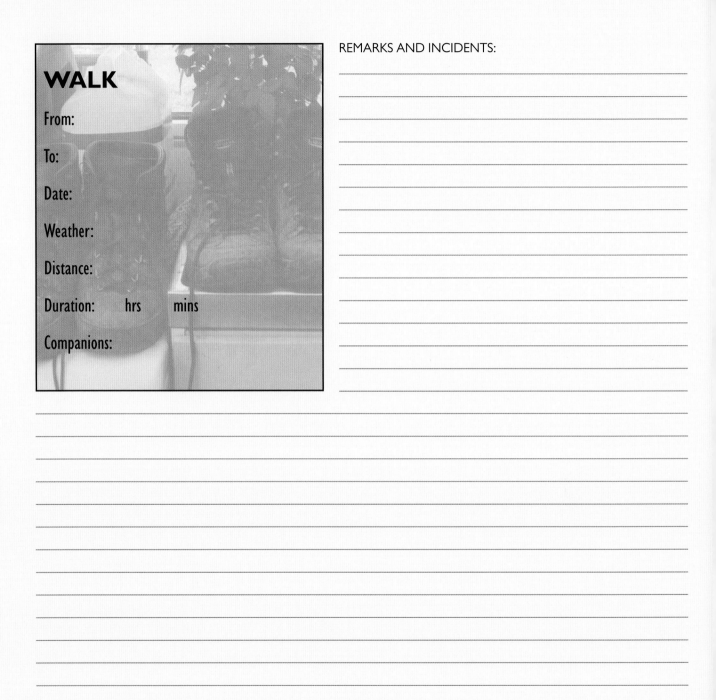

WALK

From:

To:

Date:

Weather:

Distance:

Duration: hrs   mins

Companions:

REMARKS AND INCIDENTS:

REMARKS AND INCIDENTS:

_____
_____
_____
_____
_____
_____
_____
_____
_____
_____
_____
_____
_____
_____

WALK

From:

To:

Date:

Weather:

Distance:

Duration: hrs   mins

Companions:

_____
_____
_____
_____
_____
_____
_____
_____
_____
_____
_____
_____
_____
_____

REMARKS AND INCIDENTS:

_____

_____

_____

_____

_____

_____

_____

_____

_____

_____

_____

_____

WALK

From:

To:

Date:

Weather:

Distance:

Duration: hrs   mins

Companions:

_____

_____

_____

_____

_____

_____

_____

_____

_____

_____

_____

_____

Admiring the view over Lustleigh Cleave, looking towards Bovey Tracey.
Jack Paynter

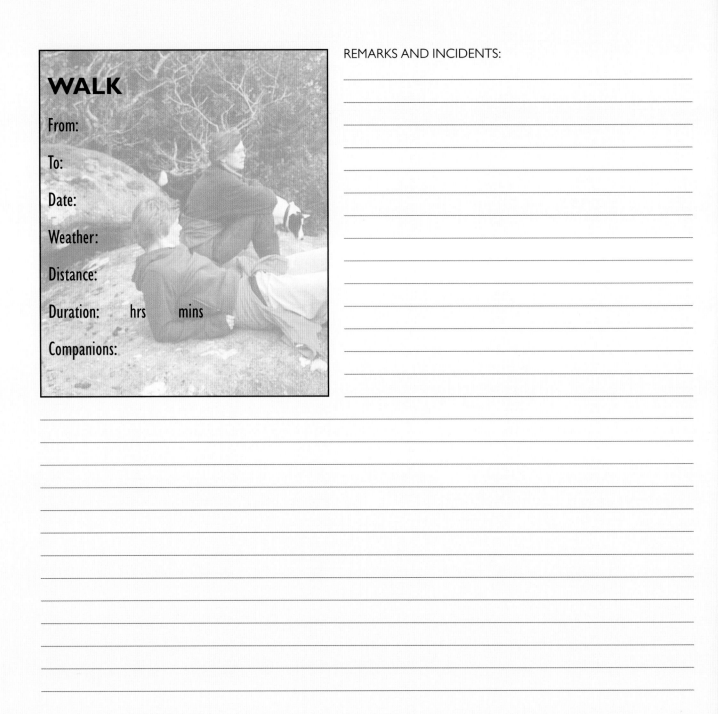

WALK

From:

To:

Date:

Weather:

Distance:

Duration:　　hrs　　mins

Companions:

REMARKS AND INCIDENTS:

REMARKS AND INCIDENTS:

_____

_____

_____

_____

_____

_____

_____

_____

_____

_____

_____

_____

_____

WALK

From:

To:

Date:

Weather:

Distance:

Duration: hrs   mins

Companions:

_____

_____

_____

_____

_____

_____

_____

_____

_____

_____

_____

_____

_____

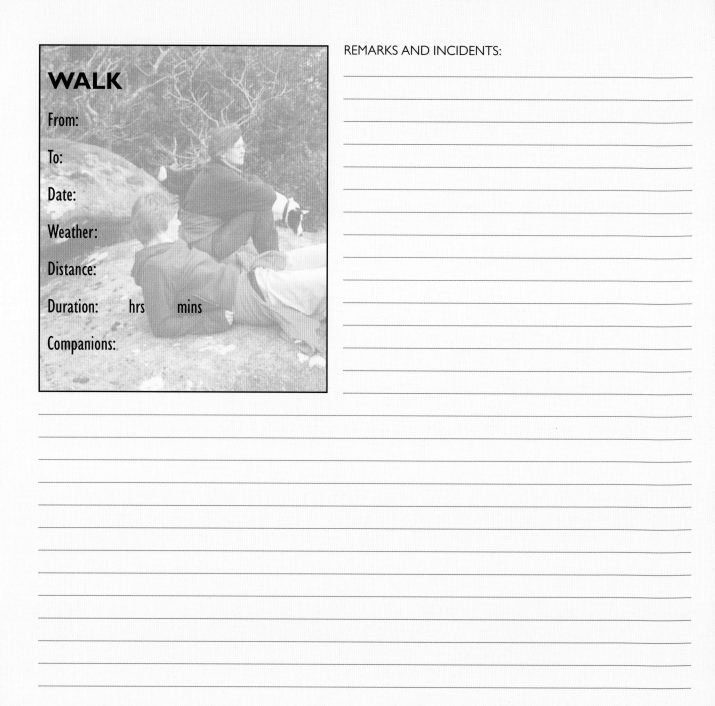

WALK

From:

To:

Date:

Weather:

Distance:

Duration: hrs   mins

Companions:

REMARKS AND INCIDENTS:

REMARKS AND INCIDENTS:

_____
_____
_____
_____
_____
_____
_____
_____
_____
_____
_____
_____
_____

WALK

From:

To:

Date:

Weather:

Distance:

Duration: hrs   mins

Companions:

_____
_____
_____
_____
_____
_____
_____
_____
_____
_____
_____
_____

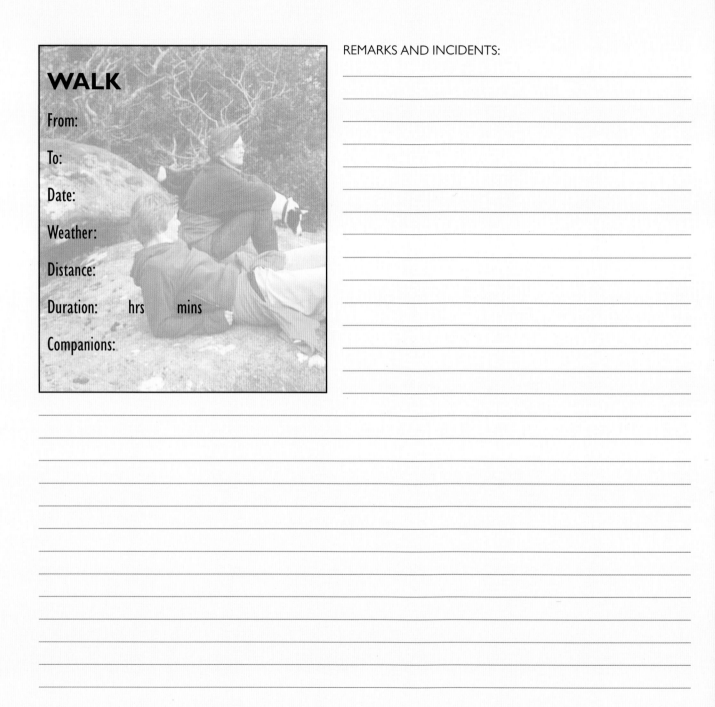

WALK

From:

To:

Date:

Weather:

Distance:

Duration: hrs   mins

Companions:

REMARKS AND INCIDENTS:

REMARKS AND INCIDENTS:

_____
_____
_____
_____
_____
_____
_____
_____
_____
_____
_____
_____
_____
_____

WALK

From:

To:

Date:

Weather:

Distance:

Duration: hrs mins

Companions:

_____
_____
_____
_____
_____
_____
_____
_____
_____
_____
_____
_____

THE PHOTOGRAPHERS

Carol Ballenger works in the landscape, both rural and urban, and produces archival quality, signed, limited edition photographs in her studio. She has exhibited widely and is a member of the Devon Guild of Craftsmen and a Fellow of the Royal Photographic Society. Her books *Dartmoor Dreams* and *Stone Universe* are published by Halsgrove. A musician and founder of Arts Live, Carol promotes various projects including live performances combining projected images, poetry and music.
Contact details: www.artslive.org.uk.
email: carol.ballenger@artslive.org.uk.

Dave Elliott is relatively new to professional photography but since retirement has established a company which produces and supplies a range of photographic products including high quality greeting cards, mounted photographic prints, and canvases. Due to the increasing demand he is now exploring having images published more widely, combining this with a passion for travel.
Contact details: www.northdevonphotography.co.uk.
email: elliott.photos@btinternet.com.

Jason Hawkes is one of the country's best-known photographers specialising in aerial photography. From his base near London he travels worldwide to produce images for books, advertising and design. Since 1991 he has provided photographs for major international companies including Nike, HSBC, Ford, Rolex, Toyota and BP. Among over twenty books he has published with Halsgrove and others are the superb aerial photography books *North Devon Coast from the Air;* and *South Devon Coast from the Air.*
Contact details: www.jasonhawkes.com.
email: library@jasonhawkes.com.

Adrian Oakes is a landscape and contemporary photographer based in Devon. He has kindled a great love and respect for Dartmoor over the last twenty years and more recently has focused on photographing its diverse landscapes and rich history. His clients include The Dartmoor National Park Authority and the National Trust who also sell prints and cards of his work. Adrian specialises in panoramas of Dartmoor and East Devon

and has had photographs published in a variety of media including *Devon Life* magazine. His books *Perfect Dartmoor* and *Dartmoor: A Winter's Tale* are published by Halsgrove. Forthcoming is a book based on his Dartmoor panoramic images.
Contact details: www.adrianoakes.com.
email: akoblackbird@hotmail.com.

Lee Pengelly was born in Plymouth in 1970 and lives and works in Devon. Lee studied a two-year course with the Bureau of Freelance Photographers, which also provided him with an understanding of the commercial side of the business and covered all the aspects of marketing his work. Using 35mm, medium and large format equipment he now supplies work to picture libraries, magazines, books, postcard and calender companies and local businesses. His books with Halsgrove include *Devon's Beautiful Buildings,* and *Devon Moods, A Portrait of Exeter* and *A Portrait of Plymouth.*
Contact: www.silverscenephoto.com.
email: Leepengelly@aol.com.

THE HALSGROVE 'BOOT UP' SERIES
Family walks for the 21st century

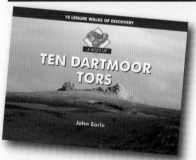

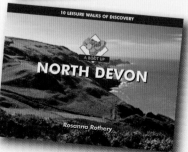

Halsgrove's popular Boot Up Series is fast becoming a phenomenon in local walks books that attract families and others to exploring the countryside in a leisurely way. It includes short walks for those living in or visiting popular areas of the country, written by those who know the region well. They aim to provide a healthy hour or two of exercise, exploring parts of Britain's countryside that the casual visitor might otherwise miss, pointing out interesting features along the way. They are perfect walks for families.
Available from all good bookshops.

For a complete list of 'Boot Ups' visit
www.halsgrove.com